THINGS TO KNOW

THE LOOK & LEARN LIBRARY

Richard Scarry's
Things To Know

GOLDEN PRESS · NEW YORK

Contents

Library of Congress Catalogue Card Number 75-151-440. © Copyright 1971 by Richard Scarry. All rights reserved. Stories and pictures in this book previously copyrighted © 1969, 1965, 1963, 1959, 1956 by Western Publishing Company, Inc. Published by Golden Press, New York, a division of Western Publishing Company, Inc. Printed in the U.S.A.

CHIPMUNK'S ABC

a is for **apple tree**.

b is for **burrow**. Guess who lives in the **burrow** under the apple tree?

C is for **Chipmunk**. It is **Chipmunk** who lives in the burrow under the apple tree.

d is for **Donkey**. Chipmunk and **Donkey** have been out picking **daffodils**.

e is for **ears**. Chipmunk's mother washes his **ears**.

9

f is for **friends**. Chipmunk has several good **friends**. **Froggie** is a **friend**.

g is for **Goat**.

Goat plays a **game** with Chipmunk.

h is for **hide-and-seek**. Chipmunk and his friends **hide** in **holes** and **hedges**.

i is for **ice cream**.

Donkey is serving **ice cream**.

j is for **jump**. Froggie **jumps** for **joy**. He loves ice cream.

k is for **kitchen**. Chipmunk puts the **kettle** on. Mouse is slicing cheese with a **knife**.

L is for **lake**. Chipmunk and Bunny go sailing on the **lake**. Both wear **life** jackets.

m is for **mumps**. **Mouse** has **mumps**.
He listens to **music** and has **meals** in bed.

n is for **net**.
Chipmunk catches butterflies in his **net**.

O is for **oboe**. Froggie plays the **oboe**. Donkey drinks from an **orange** cup.

18

p is for **party**.

Chipmunk loves **parties**. Mouse is over the mumps. He has brought Chipmunk a **present**, a bunch of **pansies**.

q is for **quilt**.

Chipmunk's mother is making a **quilt**.

r is for **river**, where Chipmunk and Donkey have a swimming **race**.

S is for **swing**.

Chipmunk likes to **swing** almost as much
as he likes to **swim**.

22

t is for **telephone**.

Someone wants to **talk** to Chipmunk.

u is for **umbrella** to keep out the sun.

v is for **vacation**. Chipmunk is at the seashore, staying in a **villa** with a nice **view** of the sea.

W is for **wagon**. Goat pulls the **wagon**, and Chipmunk rides. The **weather** is nice, and they have a **watermelon** to eat.

X is a letter. Chipmunk and Bunny play tic-tac-toe with an **X** and an O.

y is for **yellow. Yellow** flowers grow in Chipmunk's **yard**.

Z is for **zipper**. Chipmunk **zips** his jacket. He is going outside to play with his friends.

COLORS

Pink

This color is yellow.

Baby chicks are yellow.
Daffodils are yellow, too.

This color is blue.

A kitten's eyes are blue.

The sky is blue,
and so are noisy bluejays.

This color is red.

An apple is red.

This tricycle is red.

Blue and yellow make green.

A fat frog is green.

36

In summer,
leaves are green.

37

Red and yellow
make orange.

Bunny's carrot
is orange.

A pumpkin is orange, too.

Blue and red
make purple.

Violets and pansies are purple.

40

Grapes and plums are purple.

This color is brown.

Red

Yellow

Blue

Black

make brown.

Puppy's fur is brown.

This little pony is brown, too.

Red and white
make pink.

Roses and
bunny noses are pink.

44

Baby pigs are pink.

This is white.

A snowman is white,
and so is a duck.

46

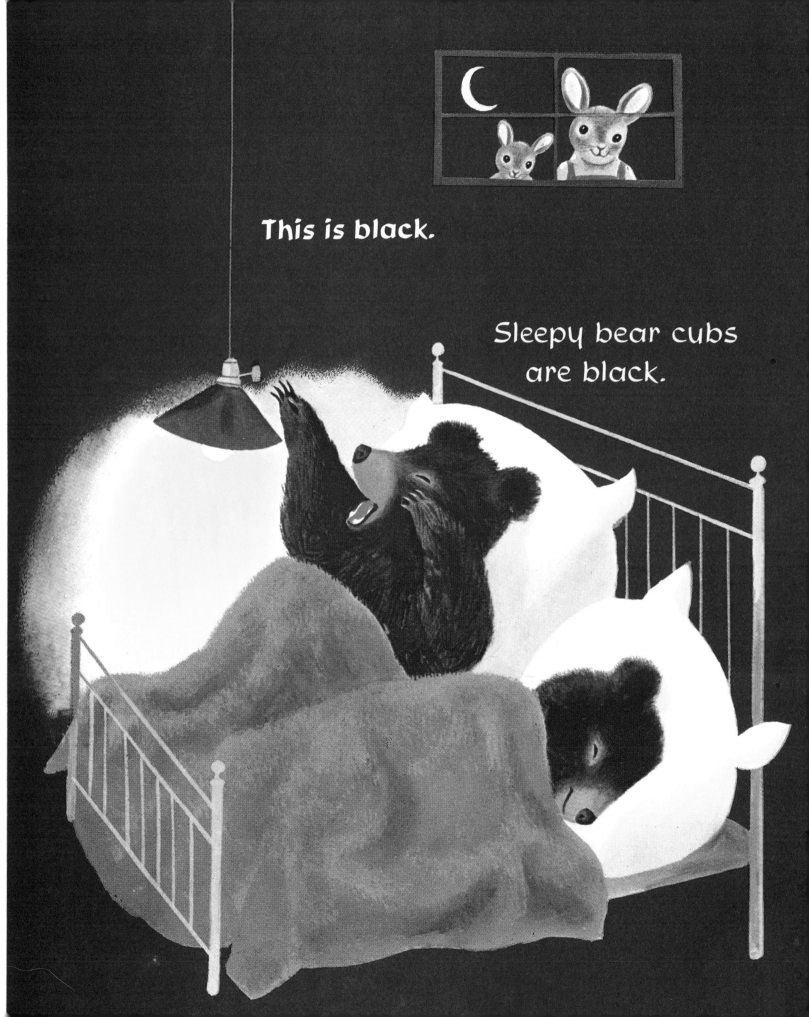

This is black.

Sleepy bear cubs
are black.

Red, yellow, blue, green—
a parrot has many colors.

Which is your favorite color?

48

THE POLITE ELEPHANT

Everyone likes the polite elephant. He knows the right things to say and do.

He tips his hat and says "Hello" when he sees his friends.

When the polite elephant
waits for the bus, he
takes his place in line.
He never pushes
or shoves.

Sometimes
the bus
is crowded.

The polite elephant always
offers his seat to a lady.

Sometimes the polite elephant goes visiting.
When someone comes
to the door, he tips
his hat and says,
"Hello, Mrs. Smith.

How are you?"

The polite elephant is a
good guest. He knows that
some rooms are for sitting
. . . and others are
for playing.

When it's time for
the polite elephant
to go home,
he remembers
to thank his friends.
"Thank you,"
he says. "I've had
a nice time."

52

The polite elephant
is polite at home,
too. He always washes
his hands and face
before sitting at
the table.

He sits straight in his chair. When
he wants something, he says, "Please."
When he gets it, he says, "Thank you."

Sometimes the polite elephant's friends come to his house. He greets them at the door. "Hello," he says. "Please come in."

He introduces them to his mother. "Mommy, this is Jimmy."

The polite elephant is a good playmate.
He shares his toys with
his friends. And he is
very careful when he plays
with someone else's toys.

When his friends leave,
the polite elephant goes
to the door with them.
"Thank you for coming,"
he says.

SHAPES
AND
SIZES

Everyone has a shape and size,
   As you can plainly see.
Big or small, short or tall—
   Which would *you* like to be?

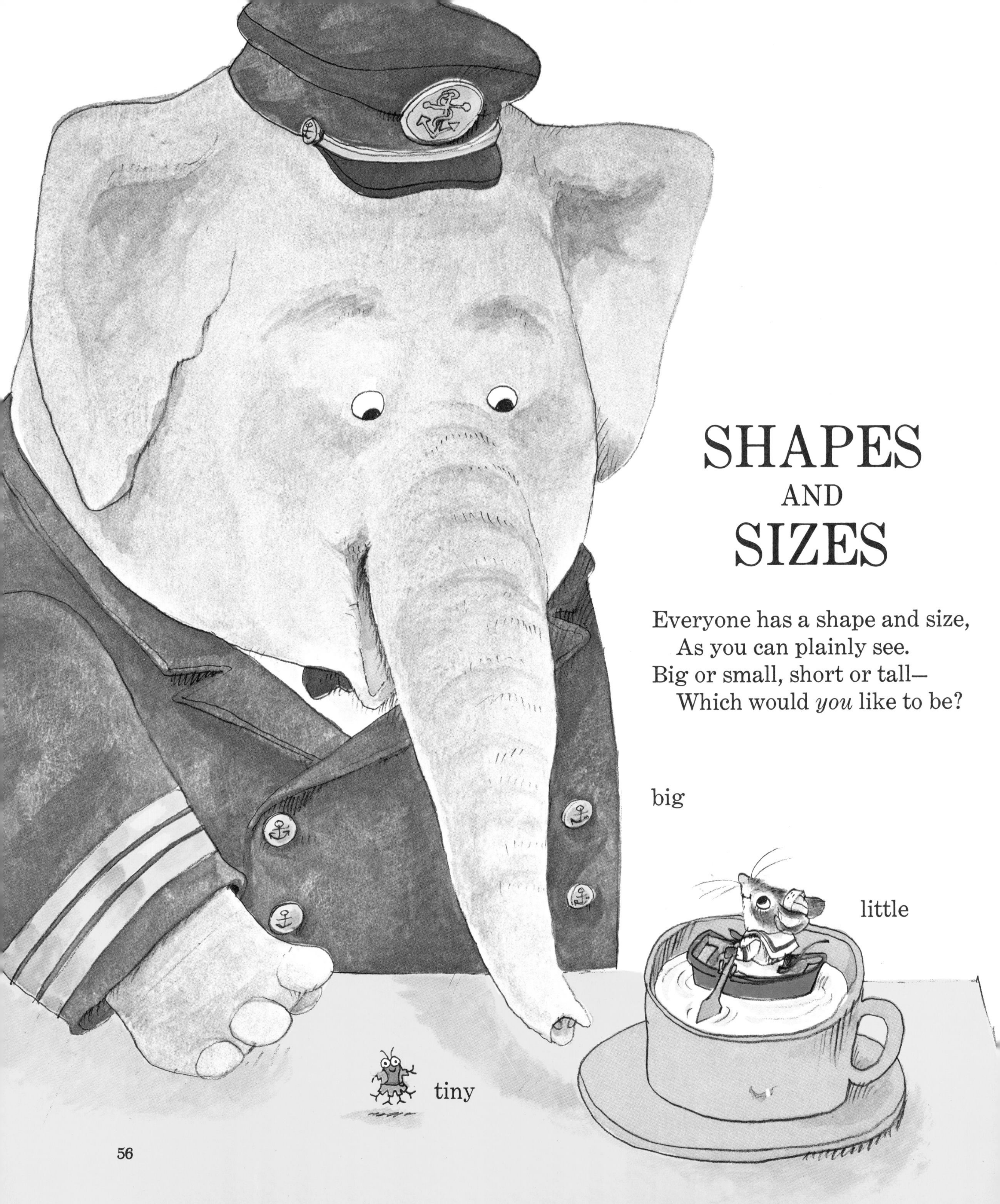

big

little

tiny

56

fat   thin

long

short

57

round

tall

Shapes and sizes everywhere—
Find a circle, find a square.
Find a triangle or star—
Find them anywhere you are.

cone

cone

short

58

SHHAPES

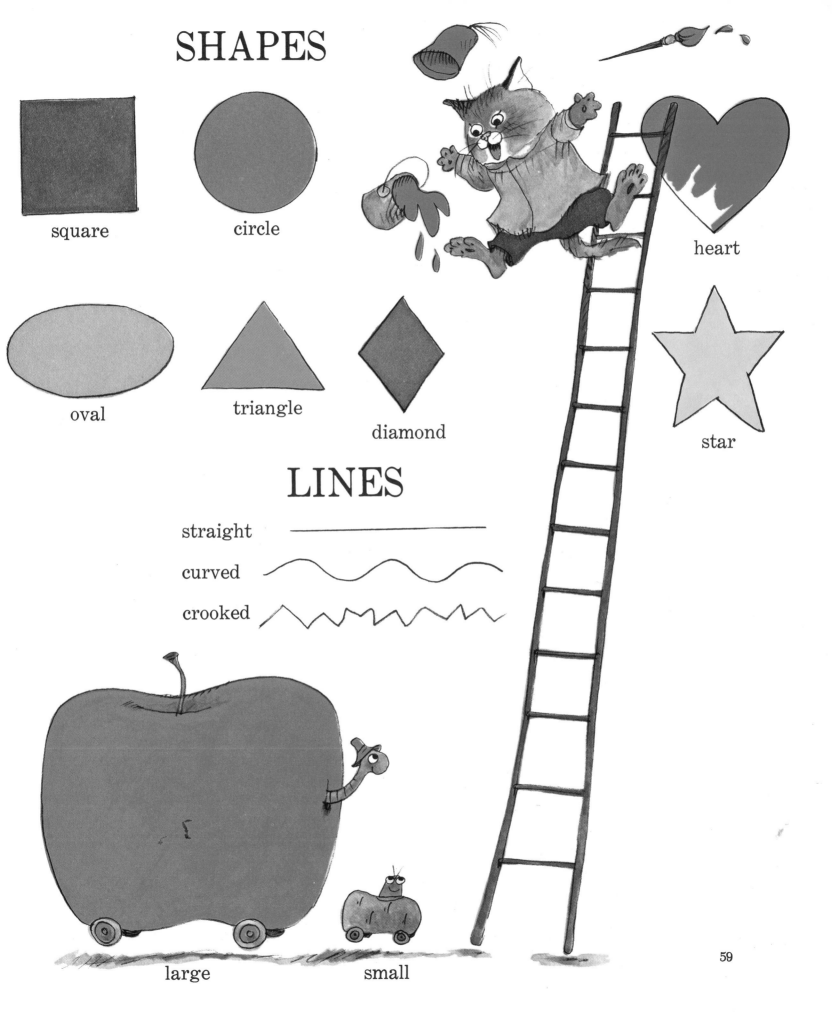

square

circle

heart

oval

triangle

diamond

star

LINES

straight

curved

crooked

large

small

59

PARTS OF THE BODY

Bear picks things up in his paws.
What do you pick things up with?

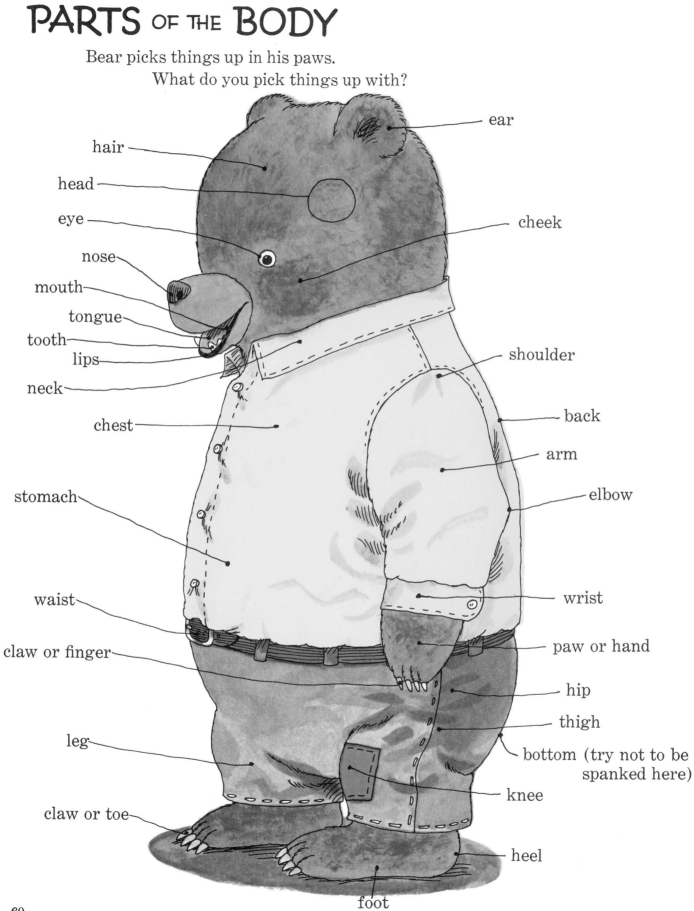

ear

hair

head

eye

cheek

nose

mouth

tongue

tooth

lips

shoulder

neck

back

chest

arm

elbow

stomach

waist

wrist

claw or finger

paw or hand

hip

thigh

leg

bottom (try not to be
spanked here)

knee

claw or toe

heel

foot

MERRY MONTHS OF THE YEAR

JANUARY

January is the first month of the year, and it starts with New Year's Day. January is a winter month, and a cold month. It's a time for coats and sweaters and scarves and boots and mittens. But there is snow for sledding and skiing, and for making snowmen. The ponds are icy and are good for skating.

Indoors, it's fun to sit in front of an open fire and pop corn and toast marshmallows.

In January, mittens drip,
And there's cocoa to sip.
This month there's a nice thing to do:
Throw crumbs to the birds!
They're hungry, too.

F·E·B·R·U·A·R·Y

February is the shortest month of the year. Most years it has only 28 days. But every four years there is Leap Year and February gets an extra day, giving it 29 days in all.

In February the nights are long and the days short. Often the sky is gray and there is slush on the ground.

But there is one day in February everybody likes, and that day is Valentine's Day. It is fun to send valentines to your friends, and it is fun to get them, too.

So be sure to watch for the mailman on February 14. He may have something very special for you.

M·A·R·C·H

March is a gusty, blustery month. The wind whistles and roars. It blows off hats and shakes trees and rattles the windows. Because of the wind, this is a good month for flying kites.

March can be icy and snowy and cold, but the robins sing "Spring is on the way!" And, sure enough, Spring always comes, and bears wake up from their long winter's sleep.

St. Patrick's Day, too, is in March. That's the day to wear shamrocks and something green.

March is supposed to come in like a lion and go out like a lamb—but sometimes it's the other way around!

A·P·R·I·L

April is a month for fun. It starts with April Fool's Day, a day for tricks and jokes. But be careful—or you may be an April Fool yourself!

And don't forget your boots and raincoat and umbrella, for April is the time for showers. The weather is full of surprises.

All month the weather teases—
Now it's warm, then, oops! the sneezes!
Take off your boots and it will shower,
Then the sun shines for an hour.
Hot and cold, rainy and sunny—
No wonder April's gay and funny!
And you know who's coming?
The Easter Bunny!

MAY

May—it's time to play outdoors again!
After all of April's showers
The world is filled with pretty flowers.
On lawns and hills and window sills
Are sunny, saucy daffodils!
And everywhere are little things
Bravely trying out new wings.
Ducks are quacky, turtles snappy.

Let's play ball!
Or better still—
   let's
     roll
      down
       a
        grassy
         hill!

J·U·N·E

June—and school is over soon!
Then all we'll do each day
Is play and play and play—
    Hooray!
Summer arrives on June 21st—
The longest day of the year.
Laze on the grass and listen—what
    do you think you'll hear?

Bees buzzing! Hummingbirds humming!
    Worms wiggling!
June is laughing, golden, giggling!
Visit the brook today.
Dip in your toes.
Perch at the edge—
And maybe a butterfly will land on
    your nose!

JULY

July begins with a *boom!*
    Sometimes it's thunder,
    With lightning in the sky.
    Sometimes the rummy-tum-tum
    Of a drummer marching by
    In the big parade down Main Street
    To celebrate the Fourth of July.
Boom, boom, boom!

You can get dressed up and carry flags
And play in your very own band.
And now it's time to make cold drinks
To sell at your lemonade stand.
These are the hot days of summer
And the sun is bright on the land.
At night, if you see a star fall,
Swiiish! Be sure to make a wish.

A·U·G·U·S·T

August is steamy, hot, ice-creamy,
Days are lazy, nights are dreamy.
Maybe you'll visit the seashore...
Play under the garden hose...
Swing in the hammock with bare toes..
Go to the woods for a picnic...
Maybe you'll pick a rose...
　　　Who knows?

Summer is nearly over, and
The birds stay up late.
Suppers are hot dogs, cooked outdoors,
So good you can hardly wait!
Listen to the birds and the insects,
Listen and you will hear them say,
"Summer, sweet summer, is nearly over,
Let's enjoy it while we may."

68

SEPTEMBER

September—and it's time for school.
Sharpen your pencils! Get your books!
Hurry! Here comes the school bus, and
you mustn't be late! Good-bye, mother!
Good morning, teacher! Here we are,
back in school again.

    Time for school, and there's a
touch of coolness in the air.

Birds are flying in the sky,
Going south. Do you know why?
Grapes are plumping, apples turn red.
Nuts are browning. It's early to bed.
Squirrels are storing nuts away.
Days are short; less time to play.
Autumn's here. The summer's gone.
Better put your sweater on.

O·C·T·O·B·E·R

October is orange and red and brown.
See the leaves come drifting down!
Rake them into piles so high
You can jump in them, and flop,
    and lie.
Now the farmer harvests his hay.
The barn is filled. Look at all the
pumpkins! Pick a big one and make

a jack-o-lantern, with eyes and nose
and a big, grinning mouth.
    Every day is growing shorter,
and every night is growing longer.
We have to wait the whole month for
    spooky Hallowe'en.
What are you going to be? A ghost?
A witch? A king or a queen?

70

N·O·V·E·M·B·E·R

November brings Thanksgiving Day
when we eat turkey and cranberries,
and drink cider, and are
thankful for all of the good things
the year has given us.
　　November smells of turkey, grapes,
　　　　and pumpkin pie,
　　And leaf-smoke curling in the sky.

Some animals burrow into the earth
To sleep until the spring.
Is a cricket sharing your house?
Can you hear him sing?
Nature's garden is resting.
The trees are stark and bare.
Now you see the lovely nests
You didn't know were there.

D·E·C·E·M·B·E·R

December is waiting and wanting and
Wishing and longing for Christmas,
The jolliest holiday of the year.
    December is the merriest month of all—
    Make a cranberry rope, a popcorn ball,
    Cookies to hang on the tree,
    Hide presents in secret places,
    Where no one could possibly see.

We try to be good all month,
So very good, as good as gold,
Because we know who's coming down
The chimney with his pack of toys
    For girls and boys.
Who is it? Can you guess?
    Yes!
    It's Santa Claus!

kite

THE SEASONS OF THE YEAR

SPRING

robin

buds

nest

tree

Look at that baby lamb hop!
It is spring. He is happy.
Look at Mr. Bear coming out of
his cave! It is spring.
Now he can use his new
lawn mower.

lamb

bush

bridge

brook

roots

cave

fern

turtle

pussy willow

spring peeper

daffodil

lawn mower

crocus

violets

73

cornfield

cow

meadow

calf

fence

SUMMER

Do you like to go
on picnics in the summertime?
Ants just love to go to picnics.
Do you know why?

station wagon

tent

fly

camp cot

screen

cooking grill

charcoal

picnic basket

cooler

hamburger

charcoal bag

ketchup

hotdog

pickle

mosquito

pole

paper cup

mustard

rock

ants

bobber

cattails

frog

dock

pond

water lily

dragonfly

74

pebbles

stones

sun

duck

falling leaves

gate

stone wall

corn shock

nuts

pumpkin
roadside stand

FALL

In the Fall the air gets
colder. The green leaves turn to
bright colors. Then they fall to
the ground. Is that why we say
it is Fall at this time of year?
Maybe it is.

Indian corn

cider

jelly

squash

basket of apples

smoke

flames

turkey

rake

bonfire

leaves

75

snowstorm

WINTER

There are many ways to
have fun on the snow and ice.
Maybe you would like to do
all of them. Would you?

sleigh

icicle

fishing
shack

skis

sled

toboggan

ice fishing

snow

ice-skating rink

snowball

hockey stick

puck

ice skates

muffler

spare tire

hockey stick

snowman

76

jeep

a pig all wrapped up

snowplow

A BEAR FOR ALL SEASONS

Bobby Bear likes the sweet smell of flowers in the springtime.

And in wintertime, he likes to ride on his sled in the snow.
He likes all the days of the year, but the day he likes best is . . .

He likes the hot, lazy days of summer.

. . . his birthday!
All his friends come and eat ice cream and birthday cake!

In the fall, he likes to play in the fallen leaves.

In what season is your birthday?

HOLIDAYS

Which holiday do you like best?
I bet you like them all.
Holidays are always very happy times,
aren't they? What did you get from
Santa Claus last Christmas?

horn

New Year's Day

valentine

St. Valentine's Day

Easter

Easter egg

Easter bunny

Easter chick

balloons

rattle

cake

ice cream

Birthday

National Holiday

fireworks

flag

bugle

fife

uniform

bass drum

drum

78

ghost

Halloween

moon

witch

skeleton

black cat

witch's broom

pumpkin

trick-or-treat bag

angel

candle

wreath

Christmas

Christmas tree

holly

ornaments

tree lights

stockings

beard

fireplace

bag

Santa Claus

present

79

THE WEATHER

sun

cloud

lightning

rain

hailstones

When we go outdoors we see what the weather is like. Sometimes it is sunny. Sometimes it is cloudy. It can be windy, or cold, or hot. It can be snowing or raining. What was the weather like outdoors today?

snowflakes

thermometer

rainbow

windmill

wind

hat

a cat chasing a hat

rain drops

toad

toadstool

ladybug

foxtail grass

puddle

mud

80

I am a
BUNNY

I am a bunny.
My name is Nicholas.
I live in a hollow tree.

In the spring, I like to pick flowers.

I lie in the grass
and watch the insects
buzzing by.

I chase the butterflies,
and the butterflies chase me.

In the summer,
I like to lie in the sun
and watch the birds.

And I like to
watch the frogs
in the pond.

**When it rains, I keep dry
under a toadstool.**

I blow the dandelion seeds
into the air.

In the fall,
I like to watch the leaves
falling from the trees.

I watch the animals
getting ready
for the winter.

And, when winter comes,
I watch the snow falling from the sky.
Then I curl up in my hollow tree
and dream about spring.

MAKING THINGS GROW

Everyone is working in the garden.
Mr. Crow has a seed in his mouth.
Do you think he will plant it?
Or will he eat it?

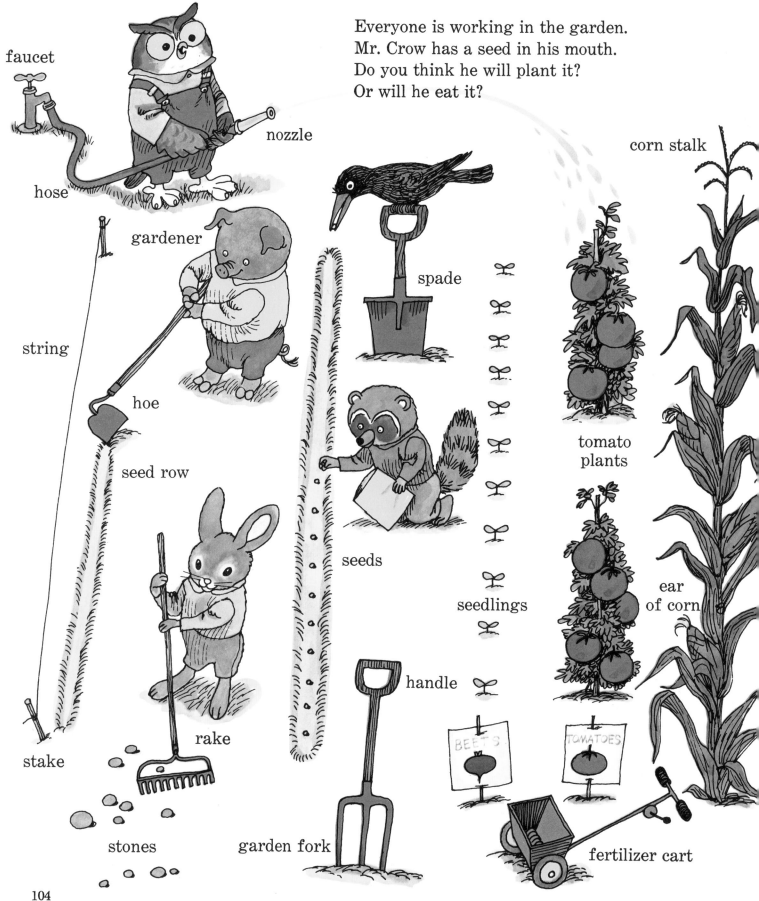

faucet

nozzle

hose

corn stalk

gardener

string

spade

hoe

seed row

tomato
plants

seeds

seedlings

ear
of corn

handle

stake

rake

stones

garden fork

BEETS

TOMATOES

fertilizer cart

PLANTING CORN

Farmer Pig planted a seed of corn in the ground.

The rain came down and wet the seed. The seed started to grow.

The sun shone down and warmed the seed. Soon, little leaves sprouted up from the ground.

It grew and grew. Finally, it had three ears of corn ready to be picked.

Farmer Pig gave one ear to Mr. Crow. He gave one ear to his wife. She loved corn.

And with his knife, Farmer Pig made the third ear into a pipe! Isn't it wonderful to think of what you can do with *one* little seed!

105

IN THE FLOWER GARDEN

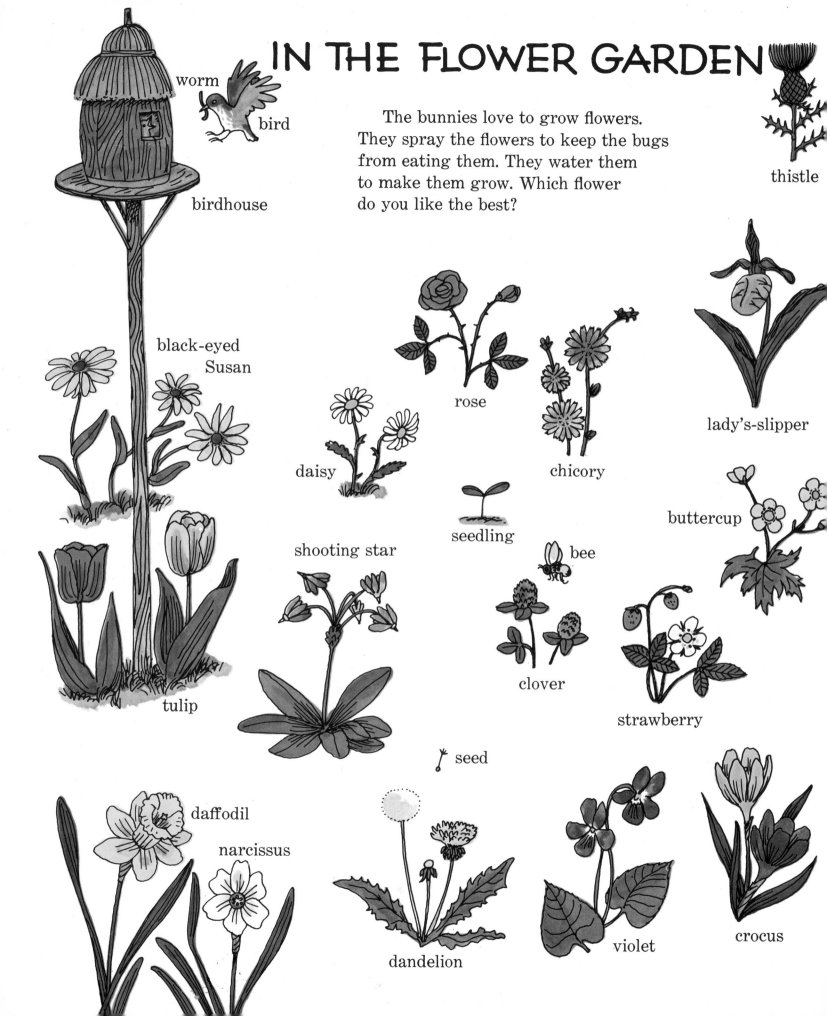

worm

bird

birdhouse

thistle

The bunnies love to grow flowers.
They spray the flowers to keep the bugs
from eating them. They water them
to make them grow. Which flower
do you like the best?

black-eyed
Susan

rose

lady's-slipper

daisy

chicory

seedling

buttercup

shooting star

bee

tulip

clover

strawberry

seed

daffodil

narcissus

dandelion

violet

crocus

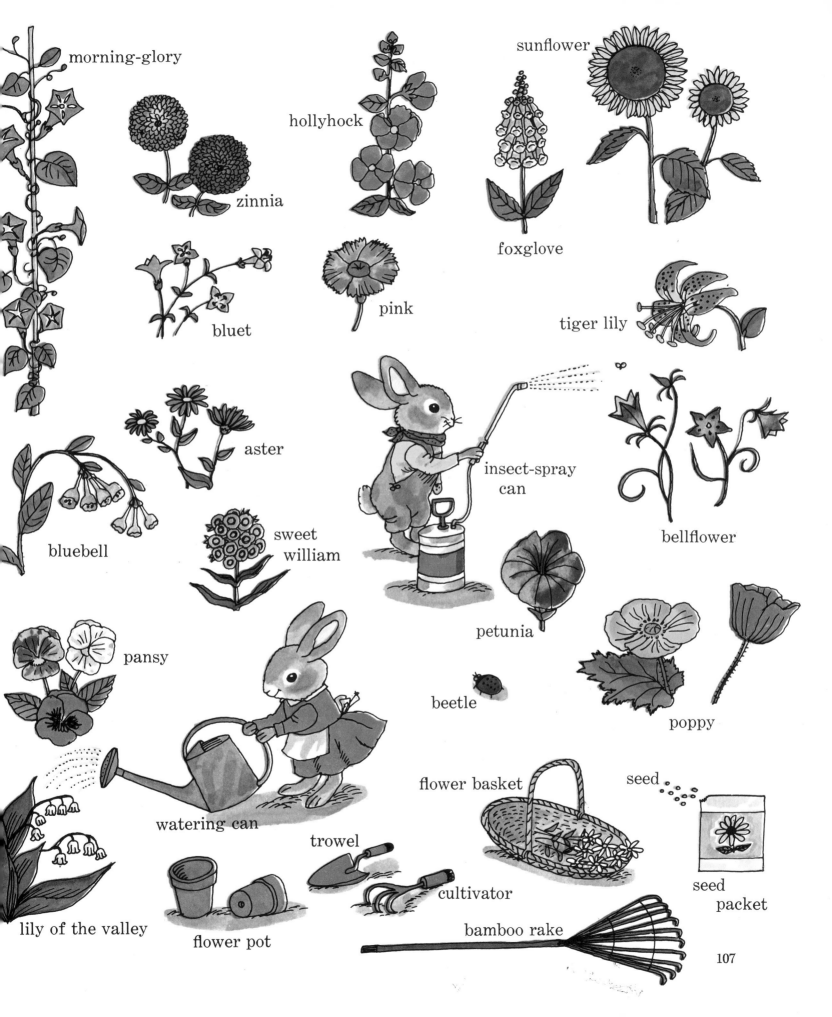

morning-glory

hollyhock

sunflower

zinnia

foxglove

bluet

pink

tiger lily

aster

insect-spray can

bellflower

bluebell

sweet william

pansy

petunia

beetle

poppy

watering can

flower basket

seed

trowel

cultivator

seed packet

lily of the valley

flower pot

bamboo rake

107

BIRDS

Most birds can fly. Some birds can't fly.
One bird who can't fly lives at the South Pole.
He likes to slide on the ice. Which bird is it?

eagle

hawk

hummingbird

barn swallow

rooster

hen

chick

nuthatch

heron

pigeon

woodpeckers

goose

duck

spoonbill

duckling

flamingo

swan

bittern

penguin

pelican

108

vulture

parrot

crow

owl

toucan

ground dove

cardinal

bluejay

puffin

robin

bluebird

sparrow

wren

sea gull

tern

sandpiper

canary

bird house

nest

baby birds

bird cage

ostrich

quail

pheasant

egret

stork

woodcock

starling

ostrich egg

WHISPER
IN MY EAR

One day Elephant went to visit Mrs. Mouse.

"I am too big to visit inside your house," he said. "Please tell me what you have inside it."

"First you must be very quiet," she said. "Then if you will lift me up with your trunk, I will whisper in your ear."

1

one

"I have **one** handsome husband inside my house," said Mrs. Mouse. "He is helping me do the housework."

One handsome husband. Is he helping with the housework?

2

two

"In my kitchen I have **two** pots. In one pot I cook meat and in the other pot I cook vegetables."
"It smells delicious," said Elephant.

Here are her two pots cooking meat and vegetables.
Mr. Mouse is tasting to see if the vegetables are done.

3
three

"How many beds do you have in your house?"
asked Elephant.
"I have **three** beds," said Mrs. Mouse in a whisper.

one

two

three

Mr. Mouse likes to make his own bed.

4
four

"I have **four** clocks
that tell the time.
My favorite one
is the cuckoo clock."

Sometimes it
frightens Mr. Mouse.

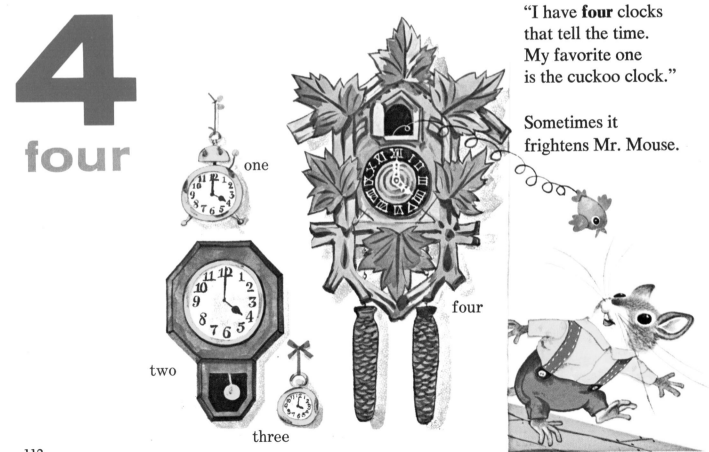

one

two

three

four

112

5
five

"In the evening when it gets dark, **five** lamps make my little house light and cheery," she said.

one   two   three   four   five

Mr. Mouse is very good at dusting the five lamps.

6
six

"In my house I have **six** chairs," whispered Mrs. Mouse. "Some are hard and some are soft."

one   two   three   four   five   six

Mr. Mouse likes to sit in a soft chair.

"I have **seven** pretty hats," she whispered in Elephant's ear.

Mr. Mouse is trying on one of her hats.

"I am a very neat housewife. I have **eight** brooms to help me keep the house clean," she whispered.

Mr. Mouse is sweeping the floor.

9
nine

"To make my house look pretty, I have **nine** plants which I water every day."

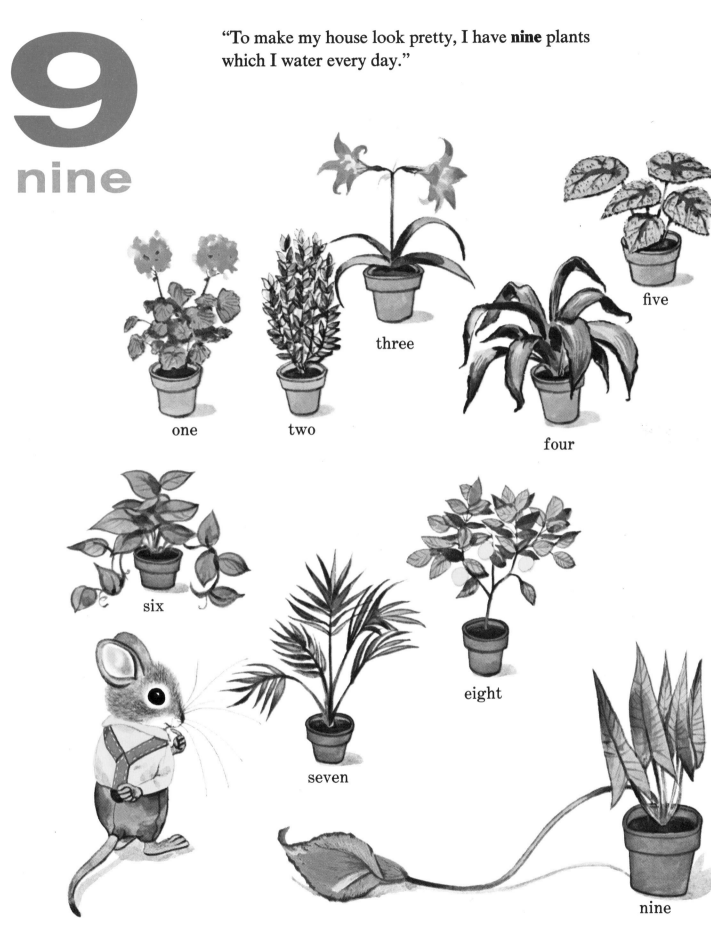

one

two

three

four

five

six

seven

eight

nine

Oh dear! Mrs. Mouse forgot to water one of her nine plants today.

ten

"I have **ten** books that I like to read,"
she whispered to Elephant.
"What are the names of your books?" asked Elephant.

one

two

three

four

five

six

seven

ten

eight

nine

Mr. Mouse likes to read books, too.
What is he reading about?

116

11
eleven

"I have **eleven** beautiful pictures hanging on my wall," she whispered.

one

two

three

four

five

six

seven

eight

nine

ten

eleven

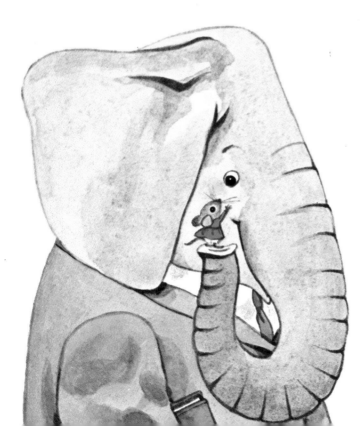

"You certainly have a very nice house," said Elephant. "But why do you have to whisper in my ear?"

"Oh, I have to whisper," said Mrs. Mouse in a whisper, "because I have **twelve** darling children who are fast asleep in the bedroom.

Turn the page and count twelve children taking their naps.

117

Can you count **twelve** children taking their naps?

12
twelve

Why don't you whisper in Mrs. Mouse's ear and tell her that the children have finished their naps and want to go out to play?

118

COUNT WITH HOOTY OWL

Hooty Owl and his mother went to the store and bought *one* piece of cheese.

They bought *two* oranges

And *three* apples.

Mother Owl picked out *four* white eggs.

What could be nicer for supper than *five* onions?

Six pickles, maybe?

They bought *seven* fat hot dogs from the butcher.

And then, home they went for supper.

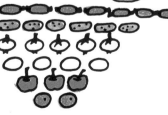

seven
six
five
four
three
two
one

"What became of that *one* piece of cheese?" asked Mother with a smile.
I think she knew.
Don't you?

119

NUMBERS

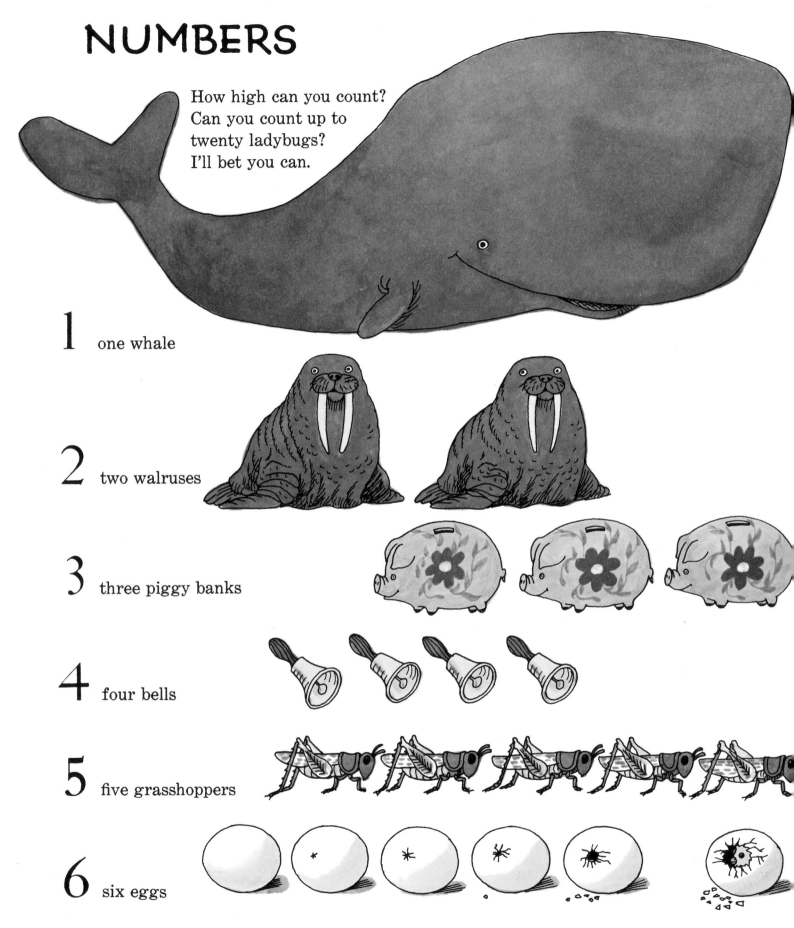

How high can you count?
Can you count up to
twenty ladybugs?
I'll bet you can.

1 one whale

2 two walruses

3 three piggy banks

4 four bells

5 five grasshoppers

6 six eggs

7   seven caterpillars

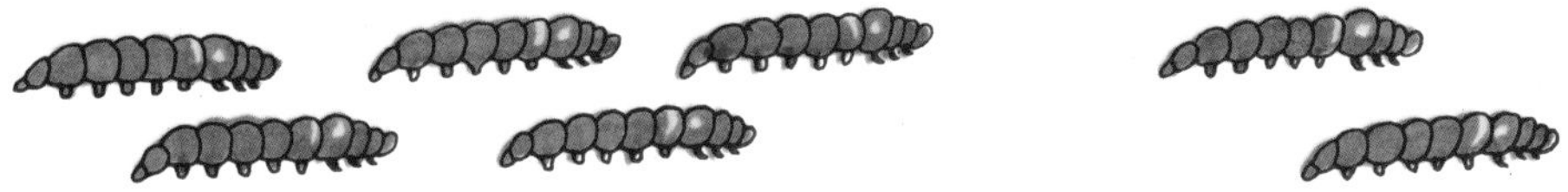

8   eight spools

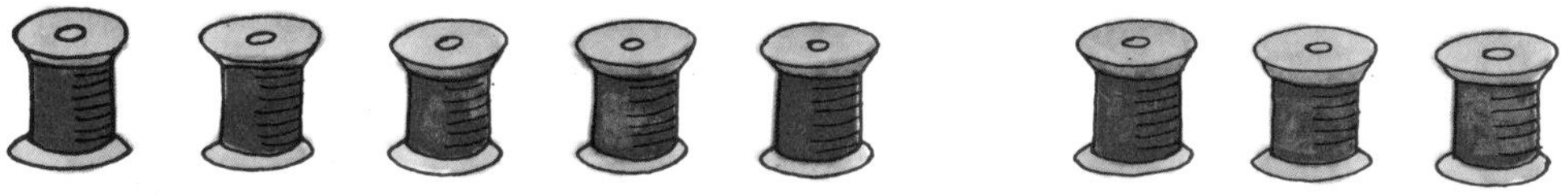

9   nine spiders

10   ten keys

11   eleven ants

12   twelve rings

13   thirteen gumdrops

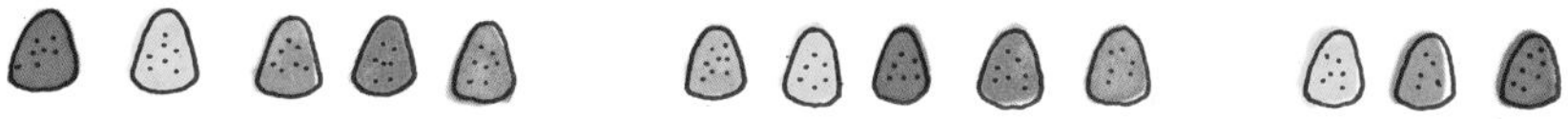

14   fourteen leaves

15   fifteen snowflakes

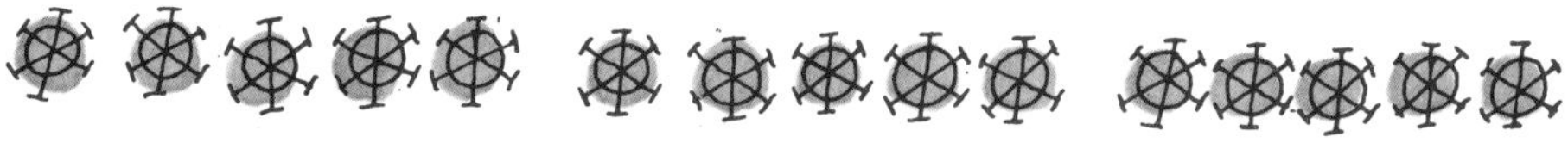

16   sixteen acorns

17   seventeen pins

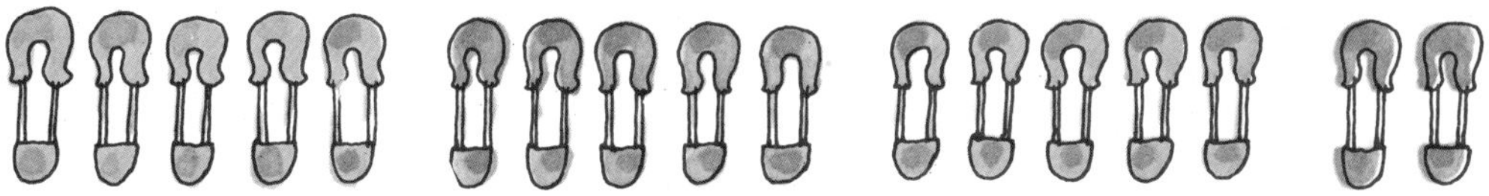

18   eighteen buttons

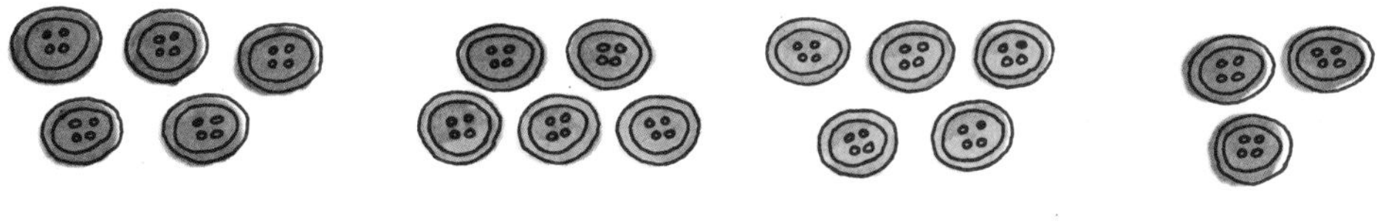

19   nineteen beads

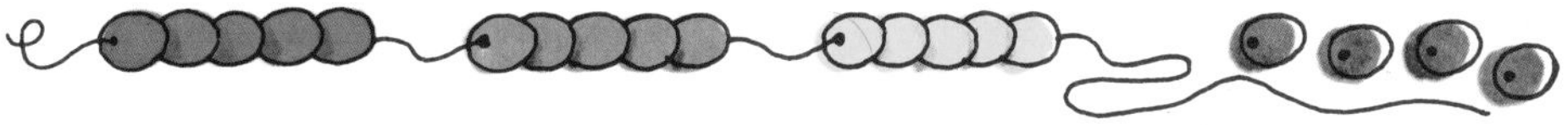

20   twenty ladybugs

curtains

sun

window

THE NEW DAY

It is the morning of a new day.
The sun is shining.
Little Bear gets up out of bed.

face cloth

soap

towel

toothbrush

toothpaste

comb

mirror

pajamas

First he washes his
face and hands.

Then he brushes
his teeth.

He combs his hair.

shirt

pants

He dresses himself.

He makes his bed.

He comes promptly
when he is called to
breakfast.

122

Bear sits up straight in his chair.

He is very hungry. This is what he eats.

cold fruit juice

warm cereal

with cream

pancakes

with butter and maple syrup

He doesn't eat the toaster.

fried eggs

bacon

toast

muffins

honey

jam

hot cocoa

cool milk

and a waffle

When he finishes eating breakfast he helps his mother to wash and dry the dishes.

cup

saucer

plate

bowl

fork

knife

spoon

glass

jar

pitcher

frying pan

lid

pot

pan

bottle

juice squeezer

glass

Now he is ready to play with his friends.

123

AT SCHOOL

School is fun. There are so many things we learn to do. Little Bear is learning how to find a lost mitten.

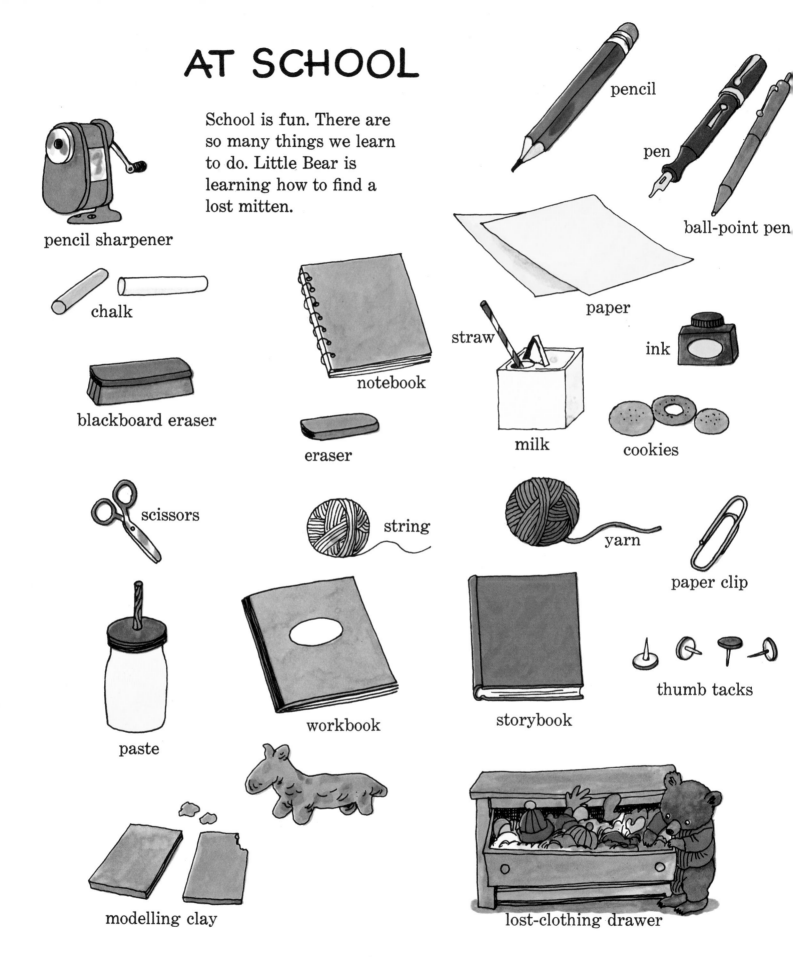

pencil sharpener

chalk

blackboard eraser

pencil

pen

ball-point pen

paper

notebook

eraser

straw

milk

ink

cookies

scissors

string

yarn

paper clip

paste

workbook

storybook

thumb tacks

modelling clay

lost-clothing drawer

flag

clock

bell

blackboard

calendar

teacher

JANUARY

a b c

cat dog

map

map stand

inkwell

waste basket

artist

pupil

desk

classroom

paper dolls

principal

hammer

nail

TOOLS

Everyone is very busy
working with his tools.
Who always carries his
tool with him?
He has a red head.

push pin

axe

ladder

log

carpenter

board

saw

sawdust

sandpaper

drill

hacksaw

vise

plane

woodpecker

wood shavings

screwdriver

screws

pliers

file

jig saw

bucksaw

trowel

bricklayer

hoe

brick wall

cement

brick

lumber

fence painter

paint brush

ball of twine

saw horse

barrel

paint

tack

tack hammer

hatchet

ruler

folding ruler

tool box

jackknife

square

putty knife

shovel

bolt

nut

dirt

monkey wrench

pick axe

compass

wheelbarrow

glue

FARMER JUNCO

Farmer Junco fed hay to his cow.

He fed grain to his horse.

He scattered corn on the ground
for his hens to eat.

He gathered eggs in the hen house.
He would have scrambled eggs for lunch.

Be careful, Farmer Junco!
Do not scramble your eggs before
you get home!

But look! Baby chicks have hatched
out of the eggs.
He will have to eat a peanut butter
sandwich instead.

NICKY GOES
TO THE DOCTOR

Nicky Bunny is going to the doctor. The
doctor's nurse meets them at the door.
"Come in!" she says.

"Hello, young man," says Dr. Doctor.
"Take off your shirt and slacks
so we can examine you."

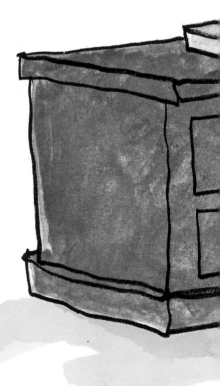

"My, how you've grown since you were here last,"
says the doctor. "Even your ears."

"You've gained weight, too," says Dr. Doctor.
"That's because I always eat everything Mommy gives me," says Nicky.

Nicky has to laugh when the doctor examines his stomach.

"Excuse me, doctor," says Nicky. "I'm ticklish."

"Perfectly normal," says the doctor.

"Now say 'A-a-ah,'" says the doctor.
"A-a-ah!" says Nicky, and the doctor looks down his throat.

The doctor looks at Nicky's ears. He takes
a long look, because Nicky has long ears.

The doctor listens to Nicky's heart. It goes
thump-thump-thump!

"Would you like to listen to my heart?" says
Dr. Doctor.

And Nicky hears the
doctor's heart go
thump-thump-thump.

The doctor taps Nicky's knee with a little hammer, and his foot jumps up by itself.

Then the doctor gives Nicky a shot.

"Ouch!" says Nicky. But he doesn't really mind.

It hardly hurts at all.

"Now we'll test your eyes," says the doctor.
He shows Nicky some pictures.

"I can see them all," says Nicky.

"You're a fine, healthy rabbit," says the doctor.
"You're growing very nicely. Get dressed and the nurse

will give you a balloon to take home."
"Thank you, doctor," says Nicky.

At home, Mrs. Bunny tells Mr. Bunny how much Nicky
has grown.

"Just keep it up," says Mr. Bunny proudly to Nicky.
"And some day you will be taller than I am."

Peter, Peter, pumpkin eater,
Had a wife and couldn't keep her;
He put her in a pumpkin shell
And there he kept her very well.

Mother Goose Rhymes

With letters we can make words.

With words we can make rhymes and stories.

Let us read some Mother Goose rhymes.

Elsie Marley is grown so fine,
She won't get up to feed the swine,
But lies in bed till eight or nine,
    Lazy Elsie Marley.

Three little kittens,
They lost their mittens,
And they began to cry,
Oh, mother dear, we sadly fear
Our mittens we have lost.

What! Lost your mittens,
You naughty kittens!
Then you shall have no pie.
Mee-ow, mee-ow, mee-ow.
No, you shall have no pie.

The three little kittens,
They found their mittens,
And they began to cry,
Oh, mother dear, see here, see he
Our mittens we have found.

What! Found your mittens,
You silly kittens!
Then you shall have some pie.
Purr-r, purr-r, purr-r,
Oh, let us have some pie.

The three little kittens,
Put on their mittens,
And soon ate up the pie;
Oh, mother dear, we greatly fear
Our mittens we have soiled.

What! Soiled your mittens,
You naughty kittens!
Then they began to sigh,
Mee-ow, mee-ow, mee-ow.
Then they began to sigh.

The three little kittens,
They washed their mittens,
And hung them out to dry;
Oh, mother dear, look here, look here,
Our mittens we have washed.

What! Washed your mittens?
You're good little kittens.
But I smell a rat close by!
Hush! Hush! Hush!
I smell a rat close by.

Little Boy Blue,
   Come blow your horn!
The sheep's in the meadow,
   The cow's in the corn.

Where is the little boy
   Tending the sheep?
He's under the haycock,
   Fast asleep.

Will you wake him?
   No, not I;
For if I do,
   He's sure to cry.

155

1

Taffy was a Welshman,
  Taffy was a thief,
Taffy came to my house
  And stole a piece of beef.

2

I went to Taffy's house,
  Taffy wasn't in,
I jumped upon his Sunday hat
  And poked it with a pin.

3

Taffy was a Welshman,
  Taffy was a sham,
Taffy came to my house
  And stole a leg of lamb.

4

I went to Taffy's house,
  Taffy was away,
I stuffed his socks with sawdust
  And filled his shoes with clay.

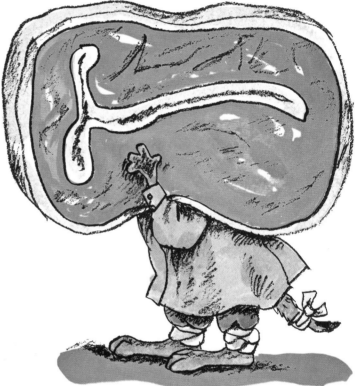

5

Taffy was a Welshman,
  Taffy was a cheat,
Taffy came to my house
  And stole a piece of meat.

6

I went to Taffy's house,
  Taffy was in bed,
I took a marrow bone
  And beat him on the head.

Pussy cat, pussy cat, where have you been?
I've been to London to look at the queen.
Pussy cat, pussy cat, what did you there?
I frightened a little mouse under her chair.

Old Mother Hubbard
Went to the cupboard
To fetch her poor dog a bone;
But when she got there
The cupboard was bare,
And so the poor dog had none.

She went to the grocer's
To buy him some fruit;
But when she came back
He was playing the flute.

She went to the hatter's
To buy him a hat;
But when she came back
He was feeding the cat.

She went to the tailor's
To buy him a coat;
But when she came back
He was riding a goat.

The dame made a curtsey,
The dog made a bow;
The dame said, Your servant,
The dog said, Bow-wow.

161

Old King Cole
Was a merry old soul,
And a merry old soul was he;
He called for his pipe,
And he called for his bowl,
And he called for his fiddlers three.

Every fiddler, he had a fine fiddle,
And a very fine fiddle had he;
Twee tweedle dee, tweedle dee, went the fiddlers.
Oh, there's none so rare
As can compare
With King Cole and his fiddlers three.

Jack Sprat could eat no fat,
His wife could eat no lean,
And so between them both, you see,
They licked the platter clean.

There was an old woman who lived in a shoe.
She had so many children she didn't know what
to do.
She gave them some broth without any bread,
And whipped them all soundly and sent them
to bed.

One, two,
Buckle my shoe;

Three, four,
Knock at the door;

Five, six,
Pick up sticks;

168

Seven, eight,
Lay them straight;

Nine, ten,
A big fat hen.

This little pig went to market,

This little pig stayed home,

170

This little pig had roast beef,   This little pig had none,

And this little pig cried, Wee-wee-wee-wee-wee,

I can't find my way home.

Barber, barber, shave a pig,
How many hairs to make a wig?
Four and twenty, that's enough.
Give the barber a pinch of snuff.

Peter Piper picked a peck of pickled peppers;
A peck of pickled peppers Peter Piper picked.
If Peter Piper picked a peck of pickled peppers,
Where's the peck of pickled peppers Peter Piper picked?

Star light, star bright,
First star I see tonight,
I wish I may, I wish I might,
Have the wish I wish tonight.

The End